Flute Exam Pack

ABRSM Grade 3

Selected from the 2018–2021 syllabus

Name

Date of exam

Contents

page

Consultant Editor for ABRSM: David Blackwell
Footnotes: Anthony Burton and Richard Jones (RJ)

Other pieces for Grade 3

LIST A
4 **Eisel** Andante *or* Paisanne (1st *or* 2nd movt from *Divertimento in D minor*). *Classical Music for Children for Flute* (Schott)

5 **Grieg** Norwegian Dance, Op. 35 No. 2, arr. Lawrance. *Winner Scores All for Flute* (Brass Wind)

6 **Handel** Presto (4th movt from *Sonata in G minor*, HWV 360, Op. 1 No. 2). *Handel: 11 Sonatas for Flute* (Bärenreiter) or *Handel: Flute Sonatas, Vol. 1* (Emerson)

7 **Mozart** Symphony No. 40: 1st movement, arr. Wedgwood. *Up-Grade! Flute Grades 2–3* (Faber)

8 **Offenbach** Champagne Song (from *La vie parisienne*), arr. McDowall. *Harlequin, Book 1* (Cramer)

9 **Shield** Old Towler, arr. Emerson. *An English Garland, Vol. 1* (Emerson)

10 **Vivaldi** Air (1st movt from *Sonata in C*, RV 48). *First Repertoire Pieces for Flute* (Boosey & Hawkes)

LIST B
4 **J. Barry** You Only Live Twice, arr. Hart. *Hartbeat* (Brass Wind)

5 **Keith Bartlett** Happy Go Lucky: from *Just for Fun! for Flute* (UMP)

6 **Gershwin** I got plenty of nothin' (from *Porgy and Bess*), arr. Harris. *Easy Gershwin for Flute* (OUP)

7 **Alan Haughton** Stroll On: from *Fun Club for Flute, Grade 2–3* (Kevin Mayhew)

8 **Mark Tanner** Gerbil's Great Escape: from *Creature Comforts, Grades 1–3* (Spartan Press)

9 **Pam Wedgwood** Scale-Learning Blues!. *Up-Grade! Flute Grades 2–3* (Faber)

10 **John Williams** Hedwig's Theme **and** Mr Longbottom Flies (from *Harry Potter and the Sorcerer's/Philosopher's Stone*), arr. Harris. *Play Hollywood for Flute* (Faber)

LIST C
4 **Sally Adams** Tarantella. No. 21 from *More Graded Studies for Flute, Book 1* (Faber)

5 **Bizet, arr. Hunt** Carmen's Song (from *Fantasia on Carmen*). *A Bizet Notebook for Solo Flute* (Spartan Press)

6 **Alan Bullard** Romantic Flute *or* Cool Flute: No. 16 *or* No. 17 from *Fifty for Flute, Book 1* (ABRSM)

7 **Oliver Ledbury** Yesterday's Song *or* Waltzer: from *Flute Salad* (Brass Wind)

8 **Helen Madden** Playing Catch Up: No. 11 from *20 Fantastic Flute Studies* (Spartan Press)

9 **Mark Nightingale** Of Mice and Keys *or* Search Engine: No. 12 *or* No. 14 from *Jazz@Etudes for Flute* (Warwick Music)

10 **James Rae** Distant Shores: No. 6 from *42 More Modern Studies for Solo Flute* (Universal)

First published in 2017 by ABRSM (Publishing) Ltd,
a wholly owned subsidiary of ABRSM, 4 London Wall Place,
London EC2Y 5AU, United Kingdom
© 2017 by The Associated Board of the Royal Schools of Music
Distributed worldwide by Oxford University Press

Music origination by Julia Bovee and Katie Johnston (Sight-reading)
Cover by Kate Benjamin & Andy Potts
Printed in England by Caligraving Ltd, Thetford, Norfolk
on materials from sustainable sources.

A:1

Menuet

Sixth movement from Suite in B minor, BWV 1067

Edited by and keyboard
transcription by Richard Jones

J. S. Bach
(1685–1750)

This elegant, graceful minuet is selected from Bach's popular Suite in B minor for flute, strings and continuo. It is one of a series of dances in the French style that follow the introductory overture. The work was written for the Leipzig collegium musicum: a vocal and instrumental ensemble made up chiefly of students, which Bach directed from 1729 to 1741. Notice how the opening slurred quaver figure in the flute part is repeatedly imitated by the continuo bass (see, for example, bars 1–2 and 9–12). (RJ) **The first repeat should be observed in the exam.**

Source: Staatsbibliothek zu Berlin, Preußischer Kulturbesitz, Mus.ms.Bach St 154, fasc. 1: MS in the hand of J. S. Bach and assistants, 1738/9. All slurs to appoggiaturas are editorial.

The Irish Washerwoman

 A:2

Arranged by David Blackwell

Trad. Irish

The Irish Washerwoman is a traditional Irish jig, sometimes sung, but more often played on the fiddle. It became well known internationally through an arrangement for orchestra made by the American composer Leroy Anderson in 1947. In David Blackwell's arrangement, when the piano takes over the tune in bars 13–20 and 29–36, the flute joins in as if partnering someone in the dance.

A:3

Alla Turca

Third movement from Piano Sonata in A, K. 331

Arranged by Alan Bullard

W. A. Mozart
(1756–91)

This is an adaptation of the finale of Mozart's Sonata in A for piano, K. 331, a work probably written in 1783. The title identifies the movement as 'in the Turkish manner', imitating Turkish military music – a popular style at the time involving a minor key, a bustling speed, insistent rhythm and, in orchestral music, noisy percussion. Initially, the excitement of this style is suggested in a stretch of music marked only *p*, but with the help of the marked slurs and staccatos. Later, the bright A major coda establishes a different mood for the jubilant ending.

Take Five

B:1

Arranged by Edward Huws Jones

Paul Desmond
(1924–77)

Take Five appeared on the 1959 LP record *Time Out* by the American modern jazz group the Dave Brubeck Quartet, and became a massive international hit. Brubeck composed most of the numbers on the album, using the unconventional time signatures for which he was renowned, but this piece in $\frac{5}{4}$ was written by the quartet's saxophonist Paul Desmond. As well as alluding to the metre, the title is a familiar instruction to musicians to take a five-minute break. The piano helpfully establishes a regular pattern of three plus two beats, which underlines the phrasing of the flute line.

Five Sets

Cinq Sets

from *Deux pièces pour flûte et piano*

Guy-Claude Luypaerts
(born 1949)

Guy-Claude Luypaerts studied the flute with Jean-Pierre Rampal at the Paris Conservatoire, leading to a career as a solo performer and teacher in the Paris area. He also studied composition, and has written a great deal of music, mostly for wind instruments in ensembles and as concerto soloists. The title of his piece *Cinq Sets* refers to the 'five sets' which is the maximum length of a match in a major tennis tournament (such as the French Open in Paris). Perhaps the regularity of the accompanying patterns and the unpredictable harmonies suggest the progress of a top-level tennis match. *Sans traîner* in bar 17 is a reminder to maintain the tempo.

From Ragtime to Riches

No. 13 from *Lucky Dip* for Flute

B:3

Mark Nightingale
(born 1967)

Mark Nightingale is a British jazz trombonist, band leader and composer. For this piece, he has delved into jazz history, adopting the syncopated (but not swung) ragtime style made popular by the piano rags of Scott Joplin in the USA in the years around 1900. The staccato markings on crotchet downbeats, for example in bar 6 and at the introduction of the new strain in bar 21, help give the music buoyancy. The title is a pun on the phrase 'from rags to riches', summarising a change from a life of poverty to one of wealth. Although the composer's metronome mark is ♩ = 160, candidates may prefer a more relaxed tempo, such as ♩ = 144.

C:1

Study in D minor

from *30 Mélodies gracieuses en forme d'études composées pour flûte seule*, Op. 10

Ludovic Leplus
(1807–late 19th cent.)

Ludovic Leplus was hailed in 1840 as one of the five most important flautists in Paris; he held various orchestral positions, ending with an 18-year period in the orchestra of the Opéra before his retirement in 1866. He composed a good deal of flute music, including several pieces in the then fashionable genre of fantasias on operatic themes, as well as a set of '30 Graceful Melodies in the form of Studies, written for solo flute and dedicated to my young pupils'. The title of 'Graceful Melodies' is a clue to how the phrases of this piece might be shaped.

Source: *30 Mélodies gracieuses en forme d'études composées pour flûte seule*, Op. 10 (Paris, n.d.) (bars 1–22). The ***p*** in bar 1 and all hairpins appear in the source; all other dynamics are editorial suggestions only.

Romany Song

No. 18 from *Skilful Studies* for Flute

C:2

Philip Sparke
(born 1951)

A graduate of the Royal College of Music in London, Philip Sparke has written extensively for brass band, wind band and student instrumentalists. His *Skilful Studies* for various instruments form, he says, 'the second volume of a progressive series of study books that takes the young wind player from beginner to accomplished musician.' The title of this study refers to the nomadic Romany people of Europe and beyond, but rather than borrowing from traditional gypsy music, the piece has a relaxed, unhurried feel.

On and Off Blues

No. 29 from *Thirty One Two Three Flute Studies*

Lynne Williams
(born 1970)

Lynne Williams is a British player and teacher of all woodwind instruments. She has published several volumes of wind ensemble pieces and studies. Her *On and Off Blues* follows the harmonic outline of the traditional twelve-bar blues, but is in a rock idiom. The rhythmic drive at different dynamic levels may be established by practising the recurring syncopated rhythmic figure, as in bar 2, against a regular beat (a metronome or tapping your foot) until it feels natural.

Scales and arpeggios

SCALES

from memory
tongued *and* slurred

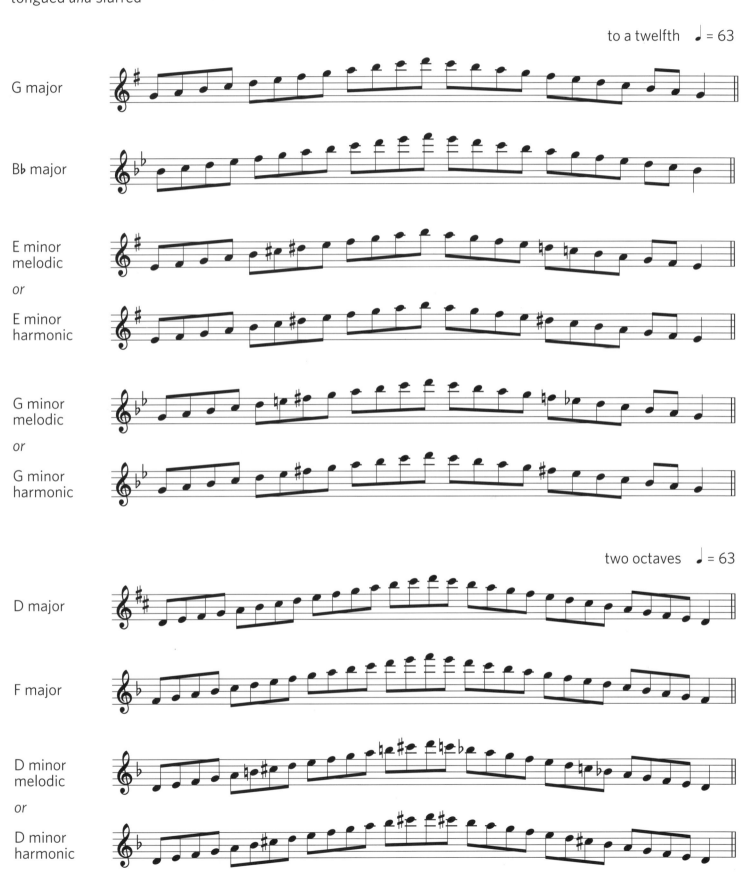

ARPEGGIOS

from memory
tongued *and* slurred

CHROMATIC SCALE

from memory
tongued *and* slurred

Sight-reading

Sight-reading

Sight-reading